Solo Début Series

Easy *Violin* Solos
Playalong Pop Hits

Julia Davis

GW00535714

Easy *Violin* Solos
Playalong Pop Hits

This publication is not authorised for sale in the
United States of America and/or Canada.

Wise Publications
part of The Music Sales Group
London/New York/Paris/Sydney/Copenhagen/Berlin/Madrid/Tokyo

Published by
Wise Publications
14-15 Berners Street, London W1T 3LJ, UK.

Exclusive Distributors:
Music Sales Limited
Distribution Centre, Newmarket Road, Bury St Edmunds, Suffolk IP33 3YB, UK.
Music Sales Pty Limited
120 Rothschild Avenue, Rosebery, NSW 2018, Australia.

Order No. AM990209
ISBN 978-1-84772-044-3
This book © Copyright 2007 Wise Publications,
a division of Music Sales Limited.

Unauthorised reproduction of any part of this publication by any means including
photocopying is an infringement of copyright.

Arranging and engraving supplied by Camden Music.
Compiled by Heather Slater.
Printed in the EU.

CD recorded, mixed and mastered by John Rose and Jonas Persson.
Instrumental solos by Simon Baggs.
New backing tracks arranged by Camden Music.
Backing tracks: 'Crazy' arranged by Danny Gluckstein;
'Patience' and 'You Give Me Something' arranged by John Maul.
Melody line arrangements by Christopher Hussey.

Your Guarantee of Quality
As publishers, we strive to produce every book to the highest commercial standards.
The music has been freshly engraved and the book has been carefully designed to minimise
awkward page turns and to make playing from it a real pleasure.
Particular care has been given to specifying acid-free, neutral-sized paper made from pulps
which have not been elemental chlorine bleached. This pulp is from farmed sustainable forests
and was produced with special regard for the environment.
Throughout, the printing and binding have been planned to ensure a sturdy, attractive
publication which should give years of enjoyment.
If your copy fails to meet our high standards, please inform us and we will gladly replace it.

www.musicsales.com

FREE bonus material downloadable to your computer.
Visit: www.hybridpublications.com
Registration is free and easy.
Your registration code is: FB705

PERFORMANCE TIPS

Welcome to this exciting collection of playalong songs, featuring some of your favourite pop hits!

Before you begin to play, make sure your instrument is in tune
(there are tuning notes on Track 1 of the CD) and listen to the demonstration performances
on Tracks 2–11 while following along with the music.

Throughout the book, you'll notice some tiny notes written into the music—these are called **cues,**
and they are not to be played. They show you what is happening on the backing track
(i.e. what the other instruments are playing) so that you will know when to come in.

There are lots of tricky semiquaver rhythms to watch out for—but don't worry,
they are much easier than they look! If you listen to original recordings of the songs
and the demonstration performances on the CD, you will get a good idea
of how they should sound and they will feel more natural to play.

Remember: always practise the passages that you find difficult on their own,
playing them slowly, but still keeping in time.

Below are some suggestions that will help you improve your performance,
including practice tips, handy 'shortcuts' to simplify the music while you are learning it,
and some hints that will make it easier to fit your performance to the CD accompaniment.

LEAVE RIGHT NOW (Will Young)

- There are some tricky rhythms to master in this song—you will find it easier if you practise each phrase on its own, and then gradually put the song together phrase-by-phrase.

- The slurs that appear throughout help to make the melody flow, and will improve the sound of your performance. However, while you are learning the song, it might help you to leave the slurs out to begin with, until you are confident with the rhythms. Try practising the opening of the first verse without slurs:

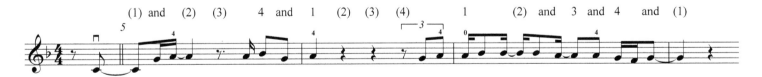

Now try playing the same passage with the slurs:

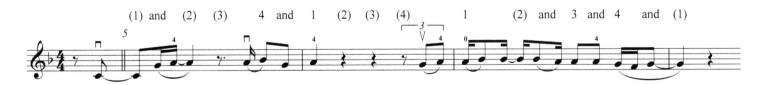

- Before you put the whole song together, make sure you understand the repeat scheme. **D.S. al Coda** at the end of bar 36 indicates that you should go back to the sign 𝄋 (bar 17) and play up to the end of bar 22, where you will see the sign **to Coda ⊕**. When you reach the **to Coda ⊕** sign, jump to the **⊕ Coda** section at bar 37.

CRAZY (Gnarls Barkley)

- There are lots of tricky semiquaver rhythms in this song, so once again practise each phrase on its own, slowly, before you put the whole song together.

- Notice that there are a number of **articulation marks** in this arrangement, which give character to the melody. There are **staccato** dots (indicating that these notes should be shorter than their written note length) and also **marcato** symbols (⌃), which indicate that the notes should be 'marked' (accented) and played slightly shorter than their written duration (but not as short as a staccato). Practise the phrase below in order to master playing staccato notes:

- An important feature of the chorus is **syncopation**. A syncopated rhythm occurs when beats of the bar which are normally unaccented are given an accent. Practise the opening phrase of the chorus, counting very carefully:

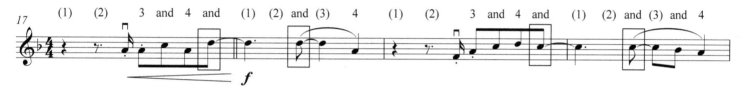

  The syncopations occur on the 'and' of the 4th beat of bar 17 and the 'and' of the 2nd beat of bar 18 (and then similarly in bars 19 and 20), beats which would normally be unaccented.

- Watch out for the **accidentals**, for example the G♯s in bar 13, and particularly the accidentals in the last line of the music—these become natural again later in the same bar.

- Make sure you understand what the **1st time bar** and **2nd time bar** symbols tell you to do—be prepared to repeat from bar 26, and go straight to the '2nd time bar' after the second time through.

DON'T CHA (Pussycat Dolls)

- The little lines above the notes, for example in bars 9, 10 and 14, are called **tenuto** marks. These indicate that you should hold these notes for their full written duration and give them a slight accent.

- This is a simple tune, but be aware of the **syncopation** in the verse section—the slurs and ties mean that many of the strong beats are not articulated:

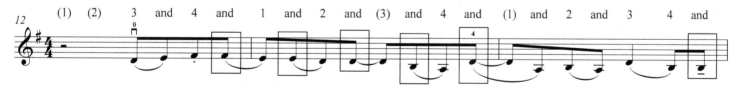

- By contrast, the chorus (beginning at bar 25) is not syncopated and should be played with confidence and bounce, which you can achieve by making the **staccato** notes shorter than their written duration.

- Make sure you understand the repeat scheme of this song: when you reach the end of the **1st time bar** in bar 40, go back to the repeat sign in bar 9 and play on, this time missing out the '1st time bar' and jumping to the **2nd time bar**. At the end of this section, **D.S. al Fine** tells you to go back to the sign 𝄋 (bar 9) and play up to the end of bar 39, where **Fine** indicates the end of the song.

- Also, notice the instruction 'On 𝄋 fade to end' in bar 33—when you play this section for the last time (on the repeat from the sign 𝄋) start fading in volume from this point until the end of the song.

FIX YOU (Coldplay)

- Look carefully at the first three phrases in this song. You will notice that they use almost the same notes, but have slightly different rhythms:

- Also have a look at the phrase from the 4th beat of bar 12, through to the double barline at the end of bar 20—it is very similar to what you have already played, with a few little changes to the notes and rhythms. Spotting similarities between phrases in music will help to make the task of learning a new piece easier.

- Now practise the first two-bar phrase of the refrain, bars 21–23, and notice that this phrase is repeated immediately in bars 23 to 25:

IS IT ANY WONDER? (Keane)

- Watch out for the assortment of articulation marks: there are **staccato**, **tenuto** and **accent** marks to think about. While you are learning the tune, don't worry about the articulation to begin with—then, once you are more confident, try adding it to improve the character of your performance. Practise the phrase below to help you master the difference between a staccato and a tenuto mark:

- The instruction 'cresc. poco a poco' in this passage tells you to gradually get louder until you reach the end of bar 25.

- The rhythms in this song are quite straightforward, but it is worth practising bars 30 and 31 in order to master the articulation and the quick semiquaver-dotted quaver rhythm on beat 4:

PATIENCE (Take That)

- This song features fast semiquaver rhythms. Practise them slowly to begin with and leave out the slurs, until you are confident enough to reintroduce the slurring. Try the opening phrases below in this way, counting very carefully to make sure you keep in time, and once you have mastered it, add in the slurs:

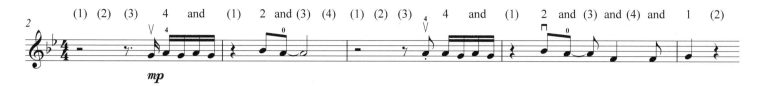

- Have a look at the repeat scheme before you start to play, so that you know how to follow the score. **D.S. al Coda** at the end of bar 34 indicates that you should go back to the sign 𝄋 (bar 15) and play until you reach **to Coda** ⊕ (at the end of bar 22). Once you have played bar 22, go straight to the ⊕ **Coda** section at bar 35.

- Watch out for the **accidentals** in the first line of the Coda (bars 35 to 37).

SOMETHING BEAUTIFUL (Robbie Williams)

- The rhythms in this song are mainly simple quaver patterns, although there are a few trickier semiquaver bits and some **syncopated** rhythms to look out for. Practise the passage below, which includes examples of both of these, and count very carefully so that you keep in time:

The notes in boxes are syncopated—that is, they are accented beats that would normally be unaccented.

- Watch out for the **accidental** F♮s in bars 11 and 15, and the **cautionary accidentals** (the bracketed sharps) before the Fs in the bars that immediately follow, which indicate that the Fs should be sharp again, as in the key signature. Also watch out for the **accidental** B♭ in bar 33.

- There is an assortment of articulation marks in the refrain, which begins on the upbeat into bar 19—there are **staccato**, **accent** and **tenuto** marks to help give the tune character. Practise the phrase below to help you master the different types of articulation:

- Notice that the second half of the refrain (upbeat into bars 27 to 34) is very similar to the first half (as above).

- In bar 43 the song changes from D major to E♭ major (modulating up a semitone)—remember that the Fs and Cs are no longer sharp and all Bs, Es and As are now flat. In addition, there are a few accidentals to watch out for in this section!

- The last note of the song, E♭, should be held for a few beats longer than its written duration, as it has a **fermata** ⌢ (pause mark) above it.

THIS LOVE (Maroon 5)

- In verse 1 (bars 9–16) and verse 2 (bars 29–36) of this song, the notes don't move very much—however, the rhythms are quite tricky. Have a listen to the demonstration performance on the CD and the original song to get an idea of how it is supposed to sound. Then practise each phrase slowly, counting very carefully, until the rhythms feel more natural to play. The first four bars of verse 1 contain most of the rhythms you'll need to know, so start by practising this passage:

- The chorus, which begins in bar 17, is marked f (forte) indicating that it should be played loudly, and also *'pesante'*, which means heavily.

UNFAITHFUL (Rihanna)

- There are lots of semiquavers in this song, which might make it look a little scary at first, but there are not too many syncopated rhythms—once you've got the idea of how it goes, it won't be as hard as it looks!

- Practise the following phrase (the upbeat into bars 13 to 16), which does include some syncopation:

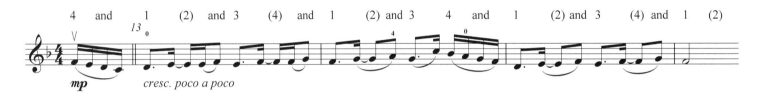

- The section from the upbeat into bar 27 to the middle of bar 38 is the second verse. If you compare it to the first verse (bar 5 to the middle of bar 16) you'll notice that it is very similar with a few added notes. Likewise, if you take a look at the last chorus (bar 48 to the middle of bar 55) you'll notice that the beginning resembles that of the first chorus (bars 17 to 24).

YOU GIVE ME SOMETHING (James Morrison)

- Practise this song phrase-by-phrase to make sure you get all of the semiquaver rhythms correct. Listen to the demonstration performance on the CD and the original song to give you a good idea of how the tune should sound.

- Try the opening four bars of the tune without the phrasing (as below) and once you have mastered the rhythms add the slurs back in:

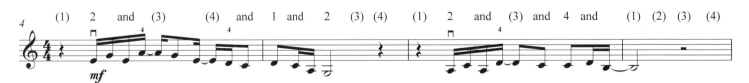

- Before you begin to play the whole song, check that you're familiar with the repeat scheme—locate where the **1st** and **2nd time bars** are, and note which passages you will need to repeat.

- In bars 42 to 43, the same three-note pattern is played three times, with slightly different rhythms. The second entry is marked *'like an echo'*, so get gradually quieter and more distant.

Leave Right Now
(Will Young)

Words & Music by Francis White

© Copyright 2003 Universal Music Publishing Limited.
All rights in Germany administered by Universal Music Publ. GmbH.
All Rights Reserved. International Copyright Secured.

Crazy
(Gnarls Barkley)

Words & Music by Thomas Callaway, Brian Burton, Gianfranco Reverberi & Gian Piero Reverberi

© Copyright 2006 Chrysalis Music Limited (35%)/Warner/Chappell Music Publishing (35%)/Atmosphere Music Limited (30%).
All Rights Reserved. International Copyright Secured.

Don't Cha
(Pussycat Dolls)

Words & Music by Thomas Callaway & Anthony Ray

With attitude! ♩ = 120

© Copyright 2005 Notting Hill Music (UK) Limited.
All Rights Reserved. International Copyright Secured.

Fine

D.S. al Fine

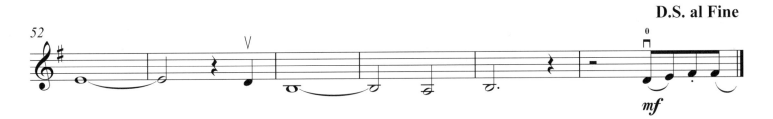

Fix You
(Coldplay)

Words & Music by Guy Berryman, Chris Martin, Jon Buckland & Will Champion

© Copyright 2005 BMG Music Publishing Limited.
All Rights Reserved. International Copyright Secured.

Is It Any Wonder?

(Keane)

Words & Music by Richard Hughes, James Sanger, Tim Rice-Oxley & Tom Chaplin

© Copyright 2006 BMG Music Publishing Limited.
All Rights Reserved. International Copyright Secured.

Patience

(Take That)

Words & Music by Mark Owen, Gary Barlow, John Shanks, Jason Orange & Howard Donald

© Copyright 2006 EMI Music Publishing Limited (33.33%)/Warner/Chappell Music North America (33.33%)/
Sony/ATV Music Publishing (UK) Limited (16.66%)/BMG Music Publishing Limited (16.66%).
All Rights Reserved. International Copyright Secured.

Something Beautiful
(Robbie Williams)

Words & Music by Robbie Williams & Guy Chambers

© Copyright 2002 BMG Music Publishing Limited (50%)/EMI Music Publishing Limited (50%).
All Rights Reserved. International Copyright Secured.

This Love
(Maroon 5)

Words & Music by Adam Levine, James Valentine, Jesse Carmichael, Mickey Madden & Ryan Dusick

With a bounce ♩ = 96

© Copyright 2002 BMG Music Publishing Limited.
All Rights Reserved. International Copyright Secured.

Unfaithful

(Rihanna)

Words & Music by Mikkel Eriksen, Tor Erik Hermansen & Shaffer Smith

Smoothly and expressively ♩ = 72

© Copyright 2006 Zomba Music Publishers Limited (50%)/Sony/ATV Music Publishing (UK) Limited (25%)/EMI Music Publishing Limited (25%).
All Rights Reserved. International Copyright Secured.

You Give Me Something
(James Morrison)

Words & Music by Francis White & James Morrison

© Copyright 2006 Sony/ATV Music Publishing (UK) Limited (50%)/Universal Music Publishing Limited (50%).
All Rights in Germany administered by Universal Music Publ. GmbH.
All Rights Reserved. International Copyright Secured.

CD Track Listing

1 Tuning notes

Full instrumental performances…

2 Leave Right Now **Will Young**
(White) Universal Music Publishing Limited.

3 Crazy **Gnarls Barkley**
(Callaway/Burton/Reverberi/Reverberi)
Chrysalis Music Limited/Warner/Chappell Music Publishing/Atmosphere Music Limited.

4 Don't Cha **Pussycat Dolls**
(Callaway/Ray) Notting Hill Music (UK) Limited.

5 Fix You **Coldplay**
(Berryman/Martin/Buckland/Champion) BMG Music Publishing Limited.

6 Is It Any Wonder? **Keane**
(Hughes/Sanger/Rice-Oxley/Chaplin) BMG Music Publishing Limited.

7 Patience **Take That**
(Owen/Barlow/Shanks/Orange/Donald)
EMI Music Publishing Limited/Warner/Chappell Music North America/Sony
/ATV Music Publishing (UK) Limited/BMG Music Publishing Limited.

8 Something Beautiful **Robbie Williams**
(Williams/Chambers) BMG Music Publishing Limited/EMI Music Publishing Limited.

9 This Love **Maroon 5**
(Levine/Valentine/Carmichael/Madden/Dusick) BMG Music Publishing Limited.

10 Unfaithful **Rihanna**
(Eriksen/Hermansen/Smith)
Zomba Music Publishers Limited/Sony/ATV Music Publishing (UK) Limited/EMI Music Publishing Limited.

11 You Give Me Something **James Morrison**
(White/Morrison) Sony/ATV Music Publishing (UK) Limited/Universal Music Publishing Limited.

Backing tracks only…

12 Leave Right Now **Will Young**
13 Crazy **Gnarls Barkley**
14 Don't Cha **Pussycat Dolls**
15 Fix You **Coldplay**
16 Is It Any Wonder? **Keane**
17 Patience **Take That**
18 Something Beautiful **Robbie Williams**
19 This Love **Maroon 5**
20 Unfaithful **Rihanna**
21 You Give Me Something **James Morrison**

To remove your CD from the plastic sleeve, lift the small lip to break the perforations. Replace the disc after use for convenient storage.